Dear Parents

As we all know, from an early age, the information our children learn about religion will later influence their beliefs, attitudes, and behaviors in later years.
This series tells about the birth, infancy, and childhood of Prophet Muhammad (peace and blessings be upon him), with stories and drawings that will appeal to our children and help them to understand.
We hope and believe that you and your children will enjoy this series and find the stories not only entertaining, but informative as well.

2

THE BEAUTIFUL BABY

It was early in the morning. The Sun was up and its light brought glory to the plateau. The lambs were bleating; the people were waking, and the new day was just beginning. Everybody felt a sense of anticipation, because today was the day that the journey to Mecca would begin. That year on the plateau there had been a drought worse than anyone could remember. As their owners prepared to go, the donkeys struggled to find something to eat. One donkey was particularly old and weak, but he had a very kind-hearted owner called Halima. While he was waiting for her to come, he said to the young donkey by his side: "This is going to be a very difficult journey for me. I am old and weak, and my legs are shaky."

4

The young donkey was healthy and strong. It was the first time that she was going to Mecca, and she was full of joy. But she wanted to make the old donkey feel better, so she said: "Don't worry, my friend. You take your time. When it is time to rest, I'll come up and stay with you." Upon hearing these words, the old donkey felt much better. Now all the preparations for the journey were complete and everybody got on their donkey and set off. The owners of the old donkey, Halima and Harith, were very kind people; they took turns riding the old donkey so as not to tire him out.

The young donkey kept her promise, and during the stops she came and rested near the old donkey. During one of these breaks, the young donkey asked: "Why are we going to Mecca, anyway?"
The old donkey answered her: "The people from the plateau regularly go to Mecca. There they find babies who need to be nursed, and they become nurse-maids for the babies."
The young donkey asked, with great curiosity: "Why don't the families nurse their own babies, instead of sending them to the plateau?"
Smiling at the question, Halima's old donkey looked upon her and said: "The milk of the mothers living in Mecca is not as plentiful as those living on the plateau, and the weather is too hot in Mecca."

8

"The weather on the plateau is beautiful. The people are well-spoken. The people in Mecca want their children to grow up in a healthier place and to learn to speak well. That is why they send their babies to the plateau when they are still very small. When they get a little bit older they go back to Mecca."
They could now see the houses of Mecca in the distance. They were all very tired, but at last they had reached Mecca. The families from the plateau spread out through the streets. Every family found a baby to take home and nurse. But Halima and Harith had come a little bit later than everyone else, and could not find a baby to nurse. The old donkey felt very bad about this.

The journey had been very hard, and now they had to return to the plateau with empty hands. The young donkey told the old donkey: "Don't feel bad, my friend. Anything you do for Allah will never go unrewarded."

Just then the old donkey saw Abdulmuttalib, a very important man in Mecca. He felt a feeling of calm and relief pass through him. He winked at his friend, the young donkey and said:

"Let's see what happens now."

Abdulmuttalib went up to Halima and said:

"I have a grandchild Muhammad whom I love very much. His father has passed away; would you consider being his nurse-maid?"

Halima talked to her husband and they both agreed to accept the baby.

11

12

The grandfather took Halima with him to Amina's house. Muhammad was such a beautiful baby, that as soon as Halima saw his glowing face she fell in love with him. She couldn't prevent herself from kissing the tiny hands and face of this beautiful baby. Baby Muhammad looked up at her smiling. But it was very hard for his mother; Amina loved her little baby so much that she found it hard to think of being separated from him for even a moment. Yet she knew that the best thing for her baby was to send him to the plateau, so reluctantly she kissed him and inhaled his scent one more time.

As the grandfather, Abdulmuttalib, held the baby out to Halima, the tears were running down Amina's face. Finally it was time to head back to the plateau and everybody got on their donkeys. Halima took the beautiful, rose-cheeked baby on her lap and got on her old donkey. At once the old donkey felt that something had started to change. He said to the young donkey: "Ohhh…What is going on? As soon as this beautiful baby got on my back I felt so much stronger. I can't believe it!"

"My legs aren't shaking anymore. I feel like I want to run, run fast and hard," he said as he began to walk faster. The old donkey overtook all the other donkeys, and left them behind. The people were very surprised by this turn of events. Even the young donkey couldn't keep up. It was as if the old donkey were flying. All the creatures looked at the old donkey, and as he passed they said:
"Run, my friend, run! You have been honored by the master of the world, Muhammad, peace and blessings be upon him."